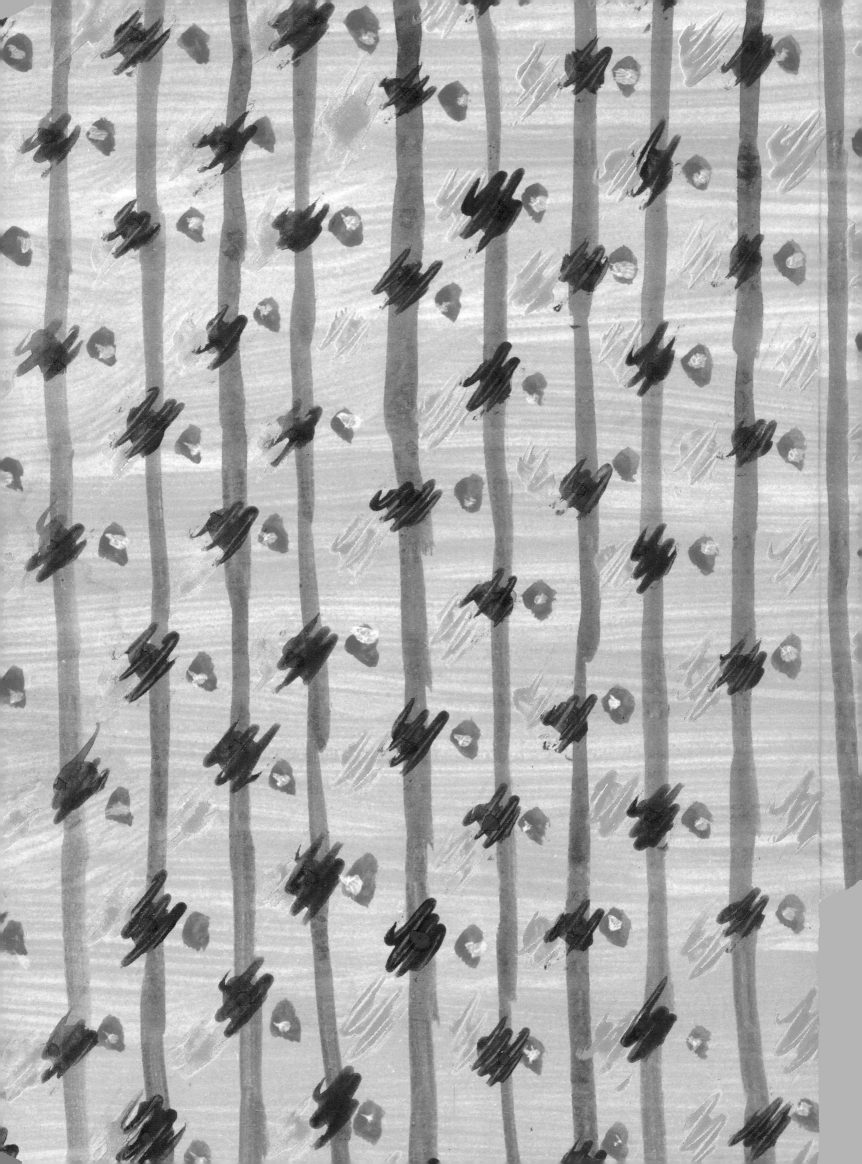

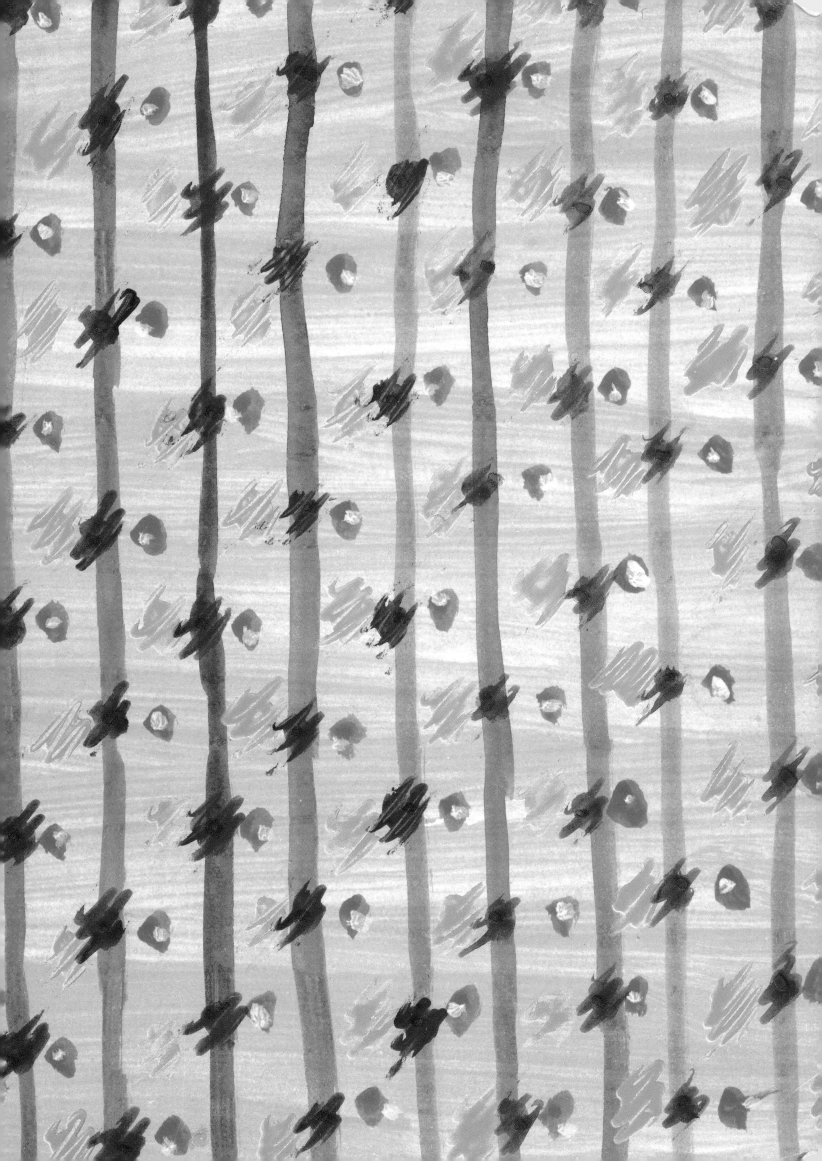

For
Susan,
Hubert
&
Andrzej

Today Is Monday Pictures by Eric Carle

SCHOLASTIC INC.

New York   Toronto   London   Auckland   Sydney

Today Is Monday
Monday, string beans

Tuesday, spaghetti
Monday, string beans

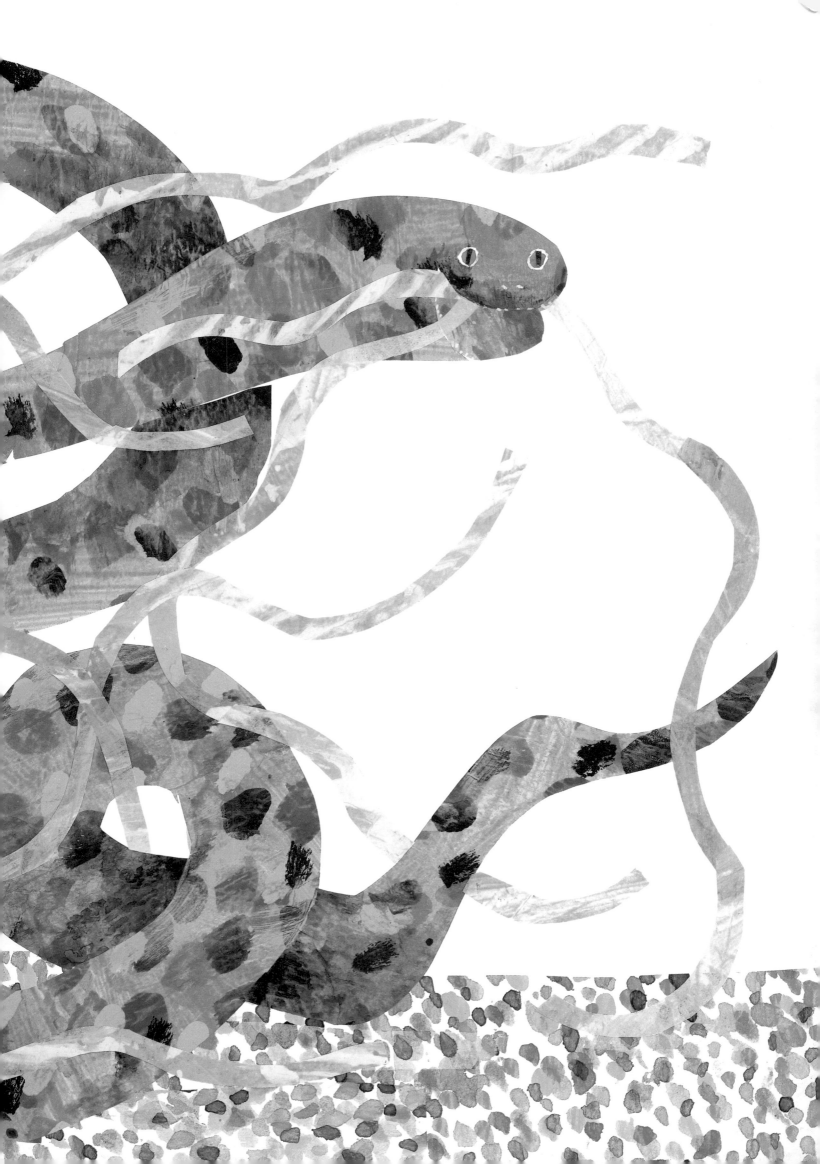

Wednesday, ZOOOOP
Tuesday, spaghetti
Monday, string beans

Thursday, roast beef
Wednesday, ZOOOOP
Tuesday, spaghetti
Monday, string beans

Friday, fresh fish
   Thursday, roast beef
   Wednesday, ZOOOOP
   Tuesday, spaghetti
   Monday, string beans

Saturday, chicken
Friday, fresh fish
Thursday, roast beef
Wednesday, ZOOOOP
Tuesday, spaghetti
Monday, string beans

Sunday, ice cream
Saturday, chicken
Friday, fresh fish
Thursday, roast beef
Wednesday, ZOOOOP
Tuesday, spaghetti
Monday, string beans

All you hungry children
Come and eat it up!

Today Is Monday

To - day   is   Mon - day, _____   to - day   is   Mon - day,

Mon - day   string   beans,   All   you   hun - gry   chil - dren,

Come   and   eat   it   up.   To - day   is   Tues - day, _   to - day   is   Tues - day,

Tues - day   spa - ghet - ti,   Mon - day   string   beans,   All   you   hun - gry   chil - dren

Come   and   eat   it   up.   To - day   is   Come   and   eat   it   up. _____

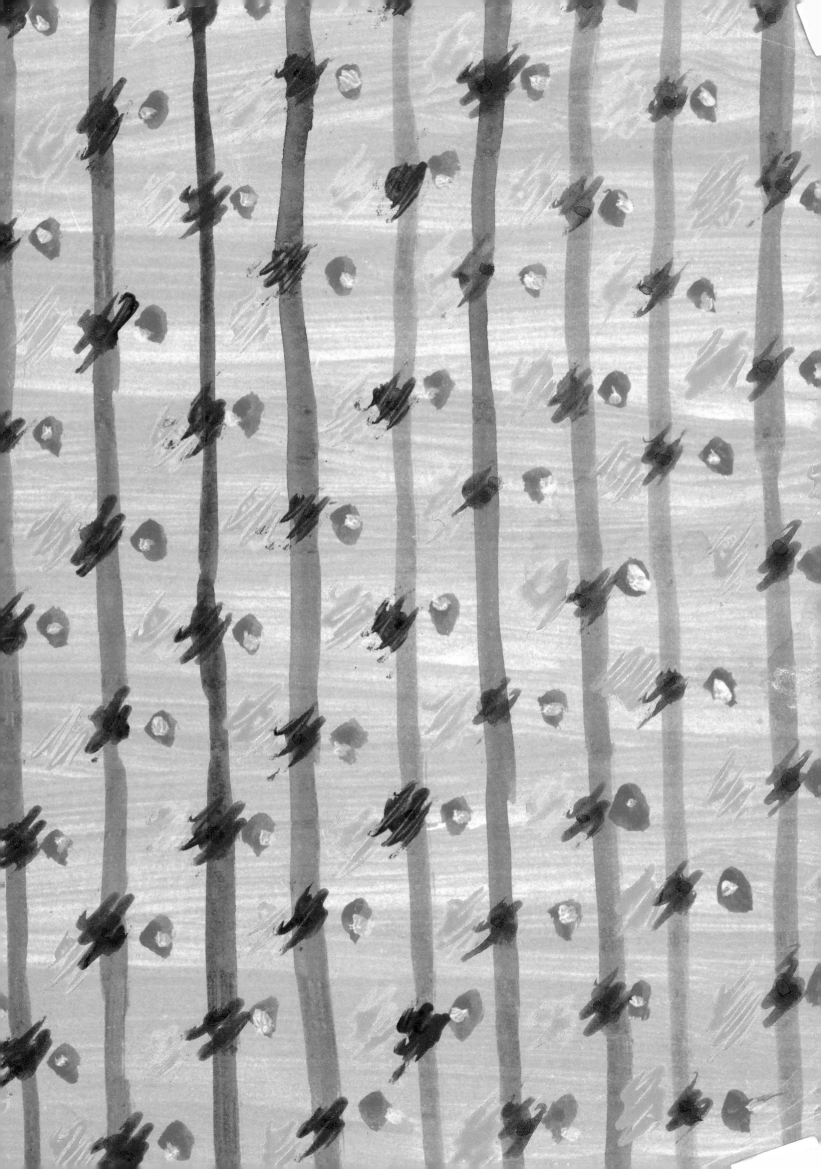